MASTER PRINTS
OF THE 20TH CENTURY

A Tribute to Jakob Rosenberg, Curator of

Prints at the Fogg Art Museum from 1939 to 1964

4 February - 31 March 1965 Fogg Art Museum

HARVARD UNIVERSITY · CAMBRIDGE

Introduction

I N OUR TIME, prints have been much pursued but not
much studied. Today, even quite recent works by quite sec-
ondary masters are soon unobtainable. Yet this is, apparently,
the first comprehensive major exhibition ever devoted to twentieth-century graphic art. Many collectors whose principal in-
terests are in other fields will pick up incidentally one or two
modern etchings or lithographs. Other collectors buy all the
graphic production of a single living artist or make a specialty
of the work of one school. Yet few even of the greatest muse-
ums have attempted to build anything more than a "representative" collection of twentieth-century prints.

These generalizations are confirmed by the titles of the pub-
lications cited in this catalogue. The prints of every major twentieth-century artist except Rouault have been listed in at least
one monograph. The same is true of work by many lesser figures, but until the publication in 1962 of the German edition of
Wolf Stubbe's *Graphic Arts in the Twentieth Century* there was
no book in any language devoted to this subject. What a con-
trast to modern painting!

How does one present a survey of contemporary prints? By
choosing something for every visitor and something from al-
most every artist? Such an approach would never have appealed
to Jakob Rosenberg. As a curator, few have equalled his zest for
acquisition. As a connoisseur, none has surpassed his sense of
discrimination. But his unique gift is his ability to rise above
even his own enthusiasm and his own perceptions. Always he
has kept in view an inclusive standard of value. His ultimate
concern has never been, "Is this object genuine or false?" "Is it
an early work or a late?" but rather "How much does it reveal
about the artist?" and "How important is that artist's achieve-

ment?" This concern has given him a special influence. Distinguished though he has long been as a teacher, his particular importance has been as a final court of appeal for the active leaders of his profession both in Europe and America. The question he has helped them to answer is the most difficult of all questions, "How much does this object matter as a work of art?"

The present exhibition shows the application of his approach to twentieth-century prints, a field in which he has been interested all his life. He chose everything included, a group of prints ranging in date from 1899 to 1962, and in place of origin from Norway to Mexico. But it is a selective rather than a representative exhibition. Jakob Rosenberg's attempt has not been to record every aspect of the field but to focus attention on what is important and boldly to affirm relative degrees of importance. Thus, of the one hundred and sixty-six prints exhibited, more than a quarter are by Picasso, less than a sixteenth were produced in the United States. Heckel is represented by four examples, Klee by only two, the same number as Orozco.

Jakob Rosenberg retired as Professor of Fine Arts at Harvard and as Curator of Prints at the Fogg Art Museum on July 1, 1964. The importance of this exhibition may suggest how deeply his colleagues regret that event. The gratitude that print collectors throughout the United States feel to him as a teacher and as an advisor is suggested by the fact that every object requested for loan was lent at once, without question, and enthusiastically—enthusiastically, but also reproachfully. Each letter of agreement said by implication, "Why did you not ask for more?"

To the lenders, one anonymous friend, Professor Frederick B. Deknatel, Associated American Artists, the Trustees of the Baltimore Museum of Art, the Museum of Fine Arts in Boston, the Art Institute of Chicago, and the Museum of Modern Art in New York, whose generosity made this exhibition possible, and to Miss Ruth Magurn, who prepared the catalogue, the Fogg Museum is deeply grateful.

JOHN COOLIDGE

EDVARD MUNCH   Norway   1863–1944

1   *Seascape*   1899   Woodcut in five colors   14 ⅝ × 22 ½
Schiefler 125. Schiefler mentions a two-colored state, but not a multi-colored one.
Fogg Art Museum (Gray Collection)

2   *Old seaman*   1899
Woodcut   17 ⅛ × 14
Schiefler 124
Museum of Fine Arts, Boston

Measurements are given in inches, height preceding width. For bibliography see Index of Artists.

3   *Nude with red hair*   1901
    Color lithograph
    19½ × 15⅝
    Schiefler 142c
    Museum of Fine Arts, Boston

4   *Madonna*   1902
    Color lithograph
    17⅜ × 17½   (after
    cutting down of the stone)
    Schiefler 33 Bb2
    Museum of Fine Arts, Boston

5   *The Kiss*   1902
    Woodcut printed from two blocks (gray and black)   18⅜ × 18 5⁄16
    Schiefler 102D
    Museum of Modern Art, New York (Gift of Abby Aldrich Rockefeller)

6 *Shore landscape* 1903 Woodcut 13 × 18 ⅛
Schiefler 210a
Baltimore Museum of Art (Blanche Adler Fund)

7 *Thorwald Stang* 1912
Lithograph 12 ⅜ × 9 ¾
Schiefler 361
Fogg Art Museum

EDOUARD VUILLARD

France 1868–1940

8 *The Cook* 1899
Color lithograph
13 ½ × 10 ⅝
From *Paysages et Intérieurs*
Roger-Marx 42
Fogg Art Museum

PIERRE BONNARD

France 1867–1947

9 *Street seen from above* 1899
Color lithograph 14 ⅝ × 8 ¾
From *Quelques aspects de la vie
de Paris*
Roger-Marx 60
Fogg Art Museum

PABLO PICASSO

Spain 1881– lives in France

10 *The frugal repast* 1904
Etching on zinc, printed in
blue (only known blue
impression) 18 ⅛ × 14 ⅞
Geiser 2 IIa
Art Institute of Chicago
(Clarence Buckingham Collection)

11 *La toilette de la mère* 1905
Etching on zinc, before steel-
facing of the plate 9 ¼ × 6 ¹⁵⁄₁₆
Inscribed "Pour Guillaume
Apollinaire, Picasso"
Geiser 15a
Lent by Dr. and Mrs. Jakob
Rosenberg

12 *Au cirque* 1905
Drypoint, before steel-facing of
the plate   8 5/8 × 5 1/2
Geiser 11a
Museum of Fine Arts, Boston
(Bequest of W. G. Russell Allen)

The Fauves

HENRI MATISSE

France   1869–1954

13 *Seated nude*   1906
Linoleum cut   18 1/2 × 15 1/8
Lieberman p. 67 (3)
Fogg Art Museum

14 *Nude seated in a folding chair* 1906
Lithograph 14 ¾ × 10 ⅝
Lieberman p. 90 (4)
Fogg Art Museum

15 *Bust of a woman with eyes closed* 1906
Lithograph 17 5/16 × 10 3/16
Lieberman p. 85
Fogg Art Museum

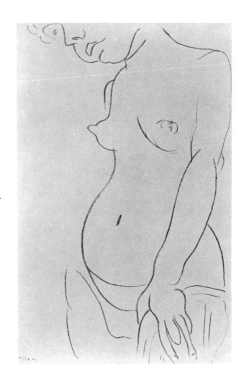

16 *Nude with face half hidden* 1914
Lithograph 19¾ × 12
Lieberman p. 94 (15)
Fogg Art Museum

NDRÉ DERAIN

rance 1880–1954

17 *Nudes in a landscape* 1906–08
Woodcut 8¼ × 10¾
Bibl. Nat. cat. 29
Fogg Art Museum (Gray Collection)

18 *Head of a woman* ab. 1910
Drypoint 12⅜ × 8⅝
Bibl. Nat. cat. 37
Fogg Art Museum (Gray Collection)

19 *Landscape* ab. 1914 Drypoint 11⅜ × 14⅛
Bibl. Nat. cat. 49
Fogg Art Museum

RAOUL DUFY   France   1877–1953

20 *Fishing*   1912   Woodcut   12½ × 15¾
    Museum of Modern Art, New York (Gift of Victor S. Riesenfeld)

MAURICE DE VLAMINCK

France   1876–1958

21 *Head of a young girl*   1915
    Color woodcut   12⅜ × 9
    Museum of Modern Art,
    New York
    (Gift of Abby Aldrich Rockefeller)

The
Early
Cubists

PABLO PICASSO

Spain 1881– lives in France

22 *Mlle. Léonie in a chaise longue*
1910 Etching and drypoint
Unique second state 7¾ × 5½
Plate III of *Saint Martorel*,
by Max Jacob
Geiser 25 II; *The Artist and
the Book* 222
Fogg Art Museum (Gift of
Meta and Paul J. Sachs)

23 *Two nude figures* 1909
Drypoint Third state
5⅛ × 4⅜
Geiser 21 IIIb
Fogg Art Museum

24 *Still life with bottle* 1912
Drypoint 19 ⅝ × 12
Geiser 33b
Fogg Art Museum

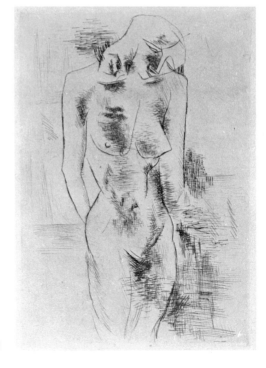

GEORGES BRAQUE

France 1882–1963

25 *Study of a nude* 1908
Drypoint 11 × 7 ⅝
Engelberts 1; Hofmann 1
Fogg Art Museum
(Gift of Meta and Paul J. Sachs)

26 *Fox* 1911
Drypoint   21 ¼ × 14 ⅝
Engelberts 5; Hofmann 5
Fogg Art Museum

LOUIS MARCOUSSIS

Poland 1883–1941 France

27 *Guillaume Apollinaire* 1912–20
Etching and drypoint 19 ½ × 10 ¾
Museum of Modern Art, New York
(Anonymous gift)

JACQUES VILLON France 1875–1963

28 *Portrait of an actor (Félix Barré)* 1913 Drypoint 15 ½ × 12 ¼
    Auberty and Perrusaux 199
    Fogg Art Museum

ERNST LUDWIG
KIRCHNER

Germany 1880–1938

29 *Dancer acknowledging applause*
ab. 1908 Color lithograph
15 1/8 × 12 3/4
Schiefler FL 81
Busch-Reisinger Museum,
Harvard University

30 *Three bathers, Moritzburg* 1907–09
Color woodcut "Probedruck"
12 × 8 3/8
Schiefler FH 128
Fogg Art Museum (Gift of
Dr. and Mrs. Jakob Rosenberg)

31 *Street scene with little dog* 1914–16
Etching 9 5/8 × 6 7/16
Schiefler Ae 180
Museum of Modern Art, New York
(Purchase)

32 *Ludwig Schames* 1917
Woodcut 22 1/8 × 11 1/2
Schiefler H 281
Fogg Art Museum (Gray Collection)

33 *Head of a cowherd (Sennkopf)* 1917
Woodcut "Handdruck" 19 5/16 × 15 5/16
Schiefler H 277
Fogg Art Museum (Gift of
Meta and Paul J. Sachs)

34 *The three paths* 1917
Woodcut "Eigendruck" 19 5/8 × 13 3/8
Schiefler H 284
Art Institute of Chicago

35 *Winter landscape in moonlig*
1919 Color woodcut
"Eigendruck" 12 × 11 3/4
Schiefler FH 360
Art Institue of Chicago

37 *The Concert* 1928
Woodcut on pink paper "Eigendruck"
17¾ × 14
Fogg Art Museum (Gray Collection)

36 *Street scene* 1922 (after a painting
of 1914) Color woodcut
"Handdruck" 27¾ × 15
Schiefler FH 469
Museum of Modern Art, New York
(Purchase)

38 *Farbentanz* 1933 Color woodcut
"Versuchsdruck" 19½ × 13 ⅞
Dube-Heynig 80
Baltimore Museum of Art
(Blanche Adler Fund)

39 *Portrait of Dr. Bauer* 1933
Color woodcut "Eigendruck"
19 ¾ × 13 ¾
Dube-Heynig 83
Fogg Art Museum (Gray Collection)

ERICH HECKEL Germany 1883–

40 *Head of a bearded man* 1908
Woodcut 9 ½ × 7 ⅝
Fogg Art Museum (Gray Collection)

41 *Bath house in the woods* 1912 Woodcut and watercolor "Handkoloriert"
12 × 15 ½
Fogg Art Museum (Gift of Dr. and Mrs. Jakob Rosenberg)

ERICH HECKEL

42 *Self-portrait* 1917
   Woodcut 14⅜ × 11¾
   Fogg Art Museum (Gray Collection)

43 *Fjord landscape* 1924 Drypoint 10 1/16 × 13 13/16
   Museum of Modern Art, New York (Gift of Abby Aldrich Rockefeller)

OTTO MÜLLER   Germany   1874–1930

44   *The finding of Moses*   ab. 1920   Color lithograph   11 ½ × 15 ⅝
Buchheim 150
Museum of Modern Art, New York (Anonymous gift)

MAX PECHSTEIN

Germany   1881–1955

45   *Somali dance*   1912   Color woodcut   13 ⅜ × 14 ¼
Fechter 106
Museum of Modern Art, New York (Purchase)

KARL SCHMIDT-ROTTLUFF   Germany   1884–

46   *Cats*   1915   Woodcut   15 5/8 × 19 1/2   From *10 Holzschnitte*
Schapire 169
Fogg Art Museum (Gift of Dr. and Mrs. Jakob Rosenberg)

47   *Way to Emmaus*   1918   Woodcut   15 5/8 × 19 5/8
From *9 Holzschnitte*
Schapire 212
Fogg Art Museum (Gray Collection)

EMIL NOLDE   Germany   1867–1956

48   *Fishing boat*   1910   Woodcut   12 × 15¾
Schiefler H 34
Fogg Art Museum (Gray Collection)

49   *Loading dock, Hamburg*   1910
Etching, aquatint, and drypoint   12 ¼ × 16 ⅜
Schiefler R 145 II
Museum of Modern Art, New York
(Gift of Abby Aldrich Rockefeller)

50 *Scribes* 1911
Etching and aquatint
10½ × 11¾
Schiefler R 154 II
Associated American
Artists, New York

51 *Prophet* 1912 Woodcut 12⅝ × 8¾
Schiefler H 110
Busch-Reisinger Museum,
Harvard University

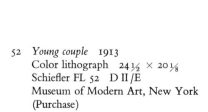

52 *Young couple* 1913
Color lithograph 24½ × 20⅛
Schiefler FL 52 D II/E
Museum of Modern Art, New York
(Purchase)

CHRISTIAN ROHLFS

Germany 1849–1938

53 *The Three Kings* ab. 1910
Woodcut 15 9/16 × 10 1/2
Vogt 22
Museum of Modern Art, New York

WILHELM LEHMBRUCK

Germany 1881–1919

54 *Seated girl with head bent* 1912
Drypoint 11 1/2 × 10 1/4
Petermann 39
Museum of Fine Arts, Boston

55 *The Prodigal Son* 1913
Drypoint 11 5/8 × 7 3/4
Petermann 74
Fogg Art Museum
(Gray Collection)

ERNST BARLACH

Germany 1870–1938

56 *The Cathedrals* 1920 Woodcut 10 × 14 From *Die Wandlungen Gottes*
Schult 165
Fogg Art Museum (Gift of Meta and Paul J. Sachs)

57 *Rebellion: the Prophet Elijah* 1922
Lithograph 20½ × 16½
From *Die Ausgestossenen*
Schult 196
Fogg Art Museum
(Gray Collection)

KÄTHE KOLLWITZ Germany 1867–1945

58 *The Mothers* 1922–23
Woodcut 13⅜ × 15¾ From *Der Krieg*
Klipstein 182 Vc
Fogg Art Museum (Gift of Winslow Ames)

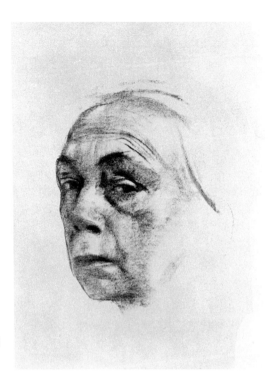

59 *Self-portrait* 1924
    Lithograph 11⅜ × 8⅝
    Klipstein 198 c
    Fogg Art Museum

60 *Death seizing a mother* 1934
    Lithograph 20⅛ × 14⅜
    From *Tod*
    Klipstein 259
    Fogg Art Museum
    (Gray Collection)

OSKAR KOKOSCHKA

Austria 1886–

61 *Self-portrait* 1914
Lithograph   Trial proof
19 ¼ × 13 ⅛ From *O Ewigkeit,*
du Donnerwort (*Bachkantate*)
Arntz 35; *The Artist and the Book* 150
Fogg Art Museum

62 *"Wohlan, soll ich . . . selig sein"* 1914
Lithograph   17 ¾ × 13 ⅜
From *O Ewigkeit, du Donnerwort*
(*Bachkantate*)
Arntz 44; *The Artist and the Book* 150
Fogg Art Museum (Gift of
Dr. and Mrs. Jakob Rosenberg)

63 *Hermine Koerner* 1920
Lithograph printed in blue
26½ × 19½
Arntz 114
Fogg Art Museum

MAX BECKMANN

Germany   1884–1950   United States

64 *Self-portrait with bowler hat* 1921
Drypoint   Second state
12¾ × 9⅝
Glaser 157; Gallwitz 153
Fogg Art Museum

65 *The tall man* 1921
Drypoint 11 ⅞ × 7 ⅞
From *Der Jahrmarkt*
Glaser 170; Gallwitz 167
Fogg Art Museum

66 *The iron bridge, Frankfurt* 1923 Drypoint 8 ½ × 10 ⅞
Gallwitz 246
Fogg Art Museum (Gray Collection)

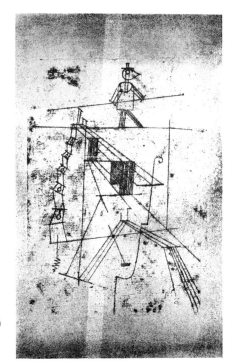

PAUL KLEE

Switzerland 1879–1940

67 *Tightrope walker* 1923
Lithograph with pink tone-plate
17⅛ × 15
Kornfeld 95
Fogg Art Museum (Gray Collection)

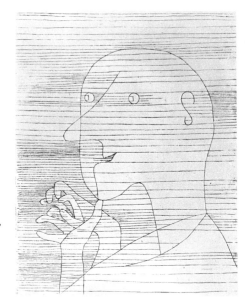

68 *Old man reckoning* 1929
Etching 11¾ × 9⅜
Kornfeld 104
Busch-Reisinger Museum,
Harvard University

FRANZ MARC

Germany 1880–1916

69 *Tiger* 1912 Woodcut 7 ⅞ × 9 ⅜
Schardt VII 2
Fogg Art Museum (Gray Collection)

OTTO DIX Germany 1891–

70 *Storm troops advancing through gas* 1924
Etching and aquatint 7 ½ × 11 ¼ From *Der Krieg*
Nierendorf cat. 81
Fogg Art Museum

GEORGE GROSZ   Germany   1893–1959   United States

71   *Factory workers*   1921   Lithograph   10½ × 15   From *Im Schatten*
Fogg Art Museum

LYONEL FEININGER

United States   1871–1956

72   *Lehnstedt*   1919   Woodcut   6¾ × 8¾
Feininger work number 1972
Fogg Art Museum

The United States

JOHN MARIN

United States   1870–1953

73 *Brooklyn Bridge no. 6*   1913
Etching and drypoint   10 ⅞ × 8 ⅞
Fogg Art Museum

74 *Woolworth Building no. 3*   1913
Etching and drypoint   12 ⅞ × 10 ½
Museum of Modern Art, New York
(Edward M. M. Warburg Fund)

LEONARD BASKIN

United States 1922–

75 *The Anatomist* 1952
Woodcut in black and red
18¾ × 11
Fogg Art Museum

ANTONIO FRASCONI Uruguay 1919– lives in the United States

76 *Clam diggers* 1954 Woodcut 18⅜ × 23¾
Fogg Art Museum (Gift of Meta and Paul J. Sachs)

GEORGE WESLEY BELLOWS   United States   1882–1925

77   *A Stag at Sharkey's*   1917   Lithograph   18 ⅝ × 23 ⅝
Inscribed "This proof for Edward Krause" (the printer)
Bellows 71
Museum of Fine Arts, Boston (Bequest of W. G Russell Allen)

BEN SHAHN   United States   1898–

78   *Silent music*   1950   Serigraph   16¾ × 35¼
Soby 56
Fogg Art Museum

Mexico

JOSÉ CLEMENTE OROZCO   Mexico   1883–1949

79   *Figures in a landscape*   ab. 1926   Lithograph   13 ½ × 17
Fogg Art Museum (Gift of E. Dudley James)

80   *La Bandera*   1928   Lithograph   10 ¼ × 16 ¾
Fogg Art Museum

DIEGO RIVERA Mexico 1886–1957

81 *Fruits of labor* 1932
Lithograph 16½ × 11¾
Fogg Art Museum

DAVID ALFARO SIQUEIROS

Mexico 1898–

82 *Moises Saenz* 1931
Lithograph 21½ × 16¼
Fogg Art Museum

LEOPOLDO MENDEZ   Mexico   1903–

83   *Deportation to death*   1942   Woodcut   13¾ × 17½
Fogg Art Museum

FRANCISCO DOSAMANTES

Mexico   1911–

84   *Women of Oaxaca*   ab. 1940
Lithograph   20¾ × 12½
Fogg Art Museum

The School of Paris

85　*Joan Massia*　1914
　　Etching　9¾ × 7⅝
　　Lieberman p. 37 (9)
　　Museum of Modern Art, New York
　　(Larry Aldrich Fund)

86　*Self-portrait*　1920–22
　　Lithograph　13 × 10
　　Art Institute of Chicago
　　(Gift of Mrs. Homer Hargrave)

HENRI MATISSE

France　1869–1954

87　*Girl with a vase of flowers*　1923
　　Lithograph　10⅞ × 7½
　　Lieberman p. 103 (51)
　　Museum of Modern Art, New York
　　(Gift of Abby Aldrich Rockefeller)

Odalisque in striped pantaloons 1925
Lithograph 21½ × 17⅜
Lieberman p. 110 (64)
Museum of Fine Arts, Boston
(Bequest of W. G. Russell Allen)

89 *Reclining nude* 1926 Lithograph 17⅜ × 21⅜
Lieberman p. 107 (84)
Fogg Art Museum (Gray Collection)

90 *Reclining dancer* 1927 Lithograph 9 ⅞ × 16 ¼
Lieberman p. 112 (96)
Fogg Art Museum (Gift of E. Dudley James)

91 *The Swan* 1932
Etching 12 × 8 ¾
From *Poésies* by Stéphane Mallarmé
The Artist and the Book 196
Museum of Modern Art,
New York (Abby Aldrich
Rockefeller Fund)

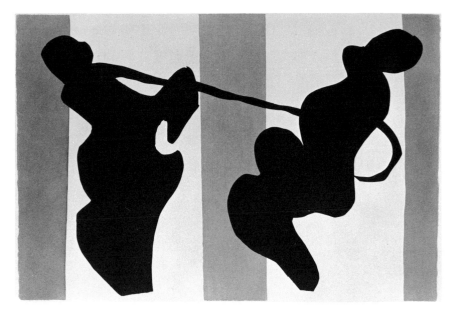

92   "*Jazz*," *Pl. XIV: "Le cowboy"*   1947   Color stencil   16½ × 25½
The Artist and the Book 200
Fogg Art Museum

93   "*Jazz*," *Pl. XV: "Le lanceur de couteaux"*   1947   Color stencil   16½ × 25½
The Artist and the Book 200
Fogg Art Museum

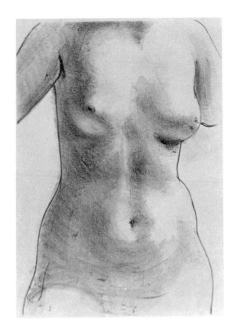

ANDRÉ DERAIN

France 1880–1954

94 *Female torso* ab. 1927
Lithograph 18⅛ × 13⅜
Bibl. Nat. cat. 74
Lent by Paul J. Sachs

RAOUL DUFY France 1877–1953

95 *"The Sea"* Pl. 4 1925 Color lithograph 14⅛ × 18½
Museum of Modern Art, New York (Abby Aldrich Rockefeller Fund)

GEORGES ROUAULT

France   1871–1958

96   *"Miserere," Pl. 8: "Who does not paint
     a face for himself?"*   ab. 1922
     Etching and aquatint over
     heliogravure   Trial proof
     22 5⁄16 × 16 15⁄16
     Museum of Modern Art, New York
     (Gift of the artist)

97   *"Miserere," Pl. 44: "My sweet
     homeland, what has become of you?"*
     1927   Etching and aquatint over
     heliogravure   16 5⁄8 × 23 1⁄2
     Fogg Art Museum

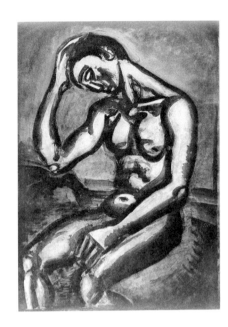

98 *"Miserere," Pl. 5: "Solitary, in this life of snares and malice"* 1927
Etching and aquatint over heliogravure 22⅝ × 16⅜
Fogg Art Museum

99 *"Miserere," Pl. 46: "The righteous, like sandalwood, perfume the axe that strikes them"* 1927
Etching and aquatint over heliogravure Trial proof
23 × 16⅝
Fogg Art Museum

100 *Paul Verlaine (posthumous portrait)*
     1933   Lithograph   16½ × 12⅜
     Fogg Art Museum

101 *Crucifixion* 1936
     Color etching and aquatint
     over heliogravure
     25½ × 19¼
     Fogg Art Museum

GEORGES BRAQUE

France 1882–1963

102 *Athena* 1932 Color lithograph,
touched with gouache
14½ × 11¾
Engelberts 13; Hofmann 15;
Mourlot 3
Museum of Fine Arts, Boston
(Bequest of W. G. Russell Allen)

103 *Helios V* 1946
Color lithograph in blue
and violet 20 × 16½
Engelberts 26; Hofmann
28; Mourlot 11
Fogg Art Museum
(Gray Collection)

104 *Chariot II* 1953 Color lithograph 19 ⅝ × 25 ⅜
Engelberts 54; Hofmann 56; Mourlot 38
Lent by Dr. and Mrs. Jakob Rosenberg

PABLO PICASSO Spain 1881– lives in France

105 *La source* 1921 Drypoint and engraving on zinc 7 × 9 ⅜
Geiser 61 II
Fogg Art Museum (Gray Collection)

PABLO PICASSO

106　*Reclining nude*　1924　Lithograph　8½ × 11¾
Geiser 238
Fogg Art Museum

107　*Scène d'intérieur*　1926　Lithograph　8⅝ × 10¾
Geiser 241
Fogg Art Museum (Gray Collection)

108 *The three friends* 1927
     Etching 16 ¼ × 11 ⅝
     Geiser 117 b
     Fogg Art Museum
     (Gray Collection)

109 *Painter and model knitting* 1927 Etching 7 ⅝ × 10 ⅞
     From *Le Chef d'Oeuvre Inconnu* by Balzac
     Geiser 126 b; *The Artist and the Book* 225
     Fogg Art Museum (Gray Collection)

PABLO PICASSO

110 *The love of Jupiter and Semele*
October 25, 1930
Etching 8¾ × 6¾
From *Les Métamorphoses* by Ovid
Geiser 148; *The Artist and the
Book* 224
Museum of Modern Art, New
York (Gift of James Thrall Soby)

111 *Nude model with bent knee* 1931
Etching 12¼ × 8¾
Geiser 208; Vollard Suite 8
Fogg Art Museum (Gift of
Meta and Paul J. Sachs)

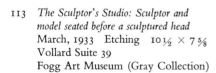

112 *The Sculptor's Studio: Sculptor,*
model, and statue of a nude
holding drapery   March 27, 1933
Etching   10 ½ × 7 ⅝
Vollard Suite 51
Fogg Art Museum

113 *The Sculptor's Studio: Sculptor and*
model seated before a sculptured head
March, 1933   Etching   10 ½ × 7 ⅝
Vollard Suite 39
Fogg Art Museum (Gray Collection)

PABLO PICASSO

114 *The Sculptor's Studio: Sculptor seated by a window, working
from model* March 31, 1933 Etching 7 ⅝ × 10 ½
Vollard Suite 59
Museum of Modern Art, New York (Purchase)

115 *The Sculptor's Studio: Three nudes
seated by a window with a basket
of flowers* April 6, 1933
Etching 14 7/16 × 11 ¾
Vollard Suite 67
Fogg Art Museum (Gray Collection

116 *The Minotaur: Minotaur caressing girl* May 18, 1933
Etching 11¾ × 14½
Vollard Suite 84
Fogg Art Museum (Gray Collection)

117 *The Minotaur: Minotaur leaning over sleeping girl*
June 18, 1933 Drypoint 11⅝ × 14⅜
Vollard Suite 93
Museum of Fine Arts, Boston

PABLO PICASSO

118   *The blind Minotaur led through the night*   1935
      Combined technique   9¾ × 13¹¹⁄₁₆
      Vollard Suite 97
      Museum of Fine Arts, Boston

119   *Minotauromachy* 1935 Etching 19½ × 27¼
     Geiser and Bolliger 89
     Museum of Modern Art, New York (Purchase)

120 *Satyr and sleeping woman* June 12, 1936 Aquatint
12½ × 16⅜
Vollard Suite 27
Fogg Art Museum (Gift of Meta and Paul J. Sachs)

121 *Dream and Lie of Franco.*
Detail January 8–
June 7, 1937 Aquatint
12½ × 16½
The Artist and the Book 228
Fogg Art Museum

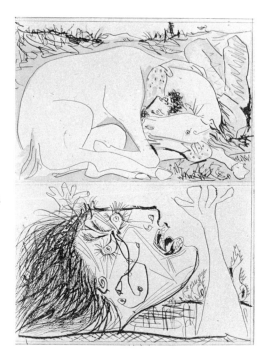

PABLO PICASSO

122 *The Ostrich* 1937
Aquatint $10\frac{1}{2} \times 8\frac{3}{8}$
From *L'Histoire Naturelle*
by Buffon, 1942
The Artist and the Book 231
Fogg Art Museum
(Gift of Joseph Pulitzer)

123 *Woman with a tambourine* 1938
Combined technique $26\frac{1}{4} \times 20$
Geiser and Bolliger 103
Art Institute of Chicago

124 *Head of a woman* 1945
Lithograph 13⅜ × 10¼
Mourlot 1
Fogg Art Museum

125 *Head of a boy* November 7, 1945
Lithograph Third state
12¼ × 9⅜
Mourlot 8
Museum of Modern Art, New York
(Curt Valentin Bequest)

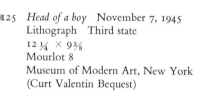

PABLO PICASSO

126 *Still life with skull and black pitcher* 1946 Lithograph 12¾ × 17⅜
Mourlot 35
Fogg Art Museum (Gray Collection)

127 *Fauns and centauress* January 26, 1947 Lithograph 19¼ × 25⅜
Mourlot 59
Fogg Art Museum

128 *Faun musician no. 4* 1948
Lithograph 26 ¾ × 20 ½
Mourlot 115
Fogg Art Museum (Gift of
Meta and Paul J. Sachs)

129 *Woman in an armchair no. 4*
(*"d'après le violet"*) 1949
Lithograph Fifth state
27 ½ × 21 ½
Mourlot 137
Fogg Art Museum
(Gray Collection)

PABLO PICASSO

130   *Lobster* 1949 Lithograph 21½ × 27½
Mourlot 143
Fogg Art Museum (Gray Collection)

131   *Figure composée II* March 8, 1949
Lithograph 24¾ × 19½
Mourlot 166
Fogg Art Museum

132 *Girl in striped blouse* April 3, 1949
Color lithograph 25½ × 19¾
Mourlot 179
Museum of Modern Art, New York
(Abby Aldrich Rockefeller Fund)

133 *Woman at a window* 1952
Aquatint 32¾ × 18½
Geiser and Bolliger 154
Lent by Mr. and Mrs.
Frederick B. Deknatel

134 *Mother and children* January 20, 1953 Lithograph 18¾ × 29¼
Mourlot 239
Fogg Art Museum (Gray Collection)

135 *Le picador* June 18, 1952 Aquatint 17 ⅞ × 21 ⅝
Geiser and Bolliger 157
Lent by Mr. and Mrs. Frederick B. Deknatel

137 *"La Tauromaquia," Pl. 18: La cogida* 1959 Aquatint 7½ × 11½
The Artist and the Book 244
Harvard College Library, Department of Printing and Graphic Arts
(Gift of Mr. and Mrs. Philip Hofer)

136 *Le jeu du taureau* February 14, 1954 Lithograph 18 ¼ × 25 ¼
Mourlot 247
Fogg Art Museum (Gift of Meta and Paul J. Sachs)

PABLO PICASSO

138   *Artist and model (La pose habillée)*
      March 19 and 26, 1954
      Lithograph   21 3/4 × 14 7/8
      Mourlot 257
      Museum of Modern Art, New York
      (Gift of Mr. and Mrs. E. Powis Jones)

139   *Portrait of D. H. Kahnweiler*
      June 3, 1957
      Lithograph   25 1/4 × 19 3/4
      Mourlot 295
      Fogg Art Museum (Gift of
      Meta and Paul J. Sachs)

140 *Head of a woman* March 16, 1962
Linoleum cut in color 25 ¼ × 21
Fogg Art Museum (Given in
memory of Howard Muellner '62)

141 *Still life with bottle and lamp* 1962
Linoleum cut in color
25 ¼ × 20 ¾
Lent by Mr. and Mrs.
Frederick B. Deknatel

FERNAND LÉGER

France 1881–1955

142 *The Vase* 1926
Color lithograph 21 × 17
Fogg Art Museum

143 *Still life with blue vase*
1951 Color lithograph
14½ × 17⅛
Museum of Modern Art,
New York (Larry Aldrich
Fund)

BERNARD BUFFET

France 1928–

144 *Fish* 1962
Drypoint 19½ × 25
Museum of Fine Arts, Boston

MARC CHAGALL

Russia 1887– lives in France

145 *Acrobat with violin* 1924
Etching and drypoint 16¼ × 12½
Meyer 63
Fogg Art Museum (Gray Collection)

146 *Self-portrait with grimace* 1924–25
     Etching and aquatint 14¾ × 10¾
     Meyer 65
     Fogg Art Museum (Gray Collection)

147 *Shaharazad's Night* 1948
     Color lithograph 14¾ × 11¼
     From *Four Tales from the Arabian Nights*
     Cain and Mourlot 48
     Fogg Art Museum
     (Gift of Meta and Paul J. Sachs)

England

GRAHAM SUTHERLAND

England 1903–

148 *Bird* 1954
     Color lithograph 17⅛ × 17⅜
     Fogg Art Museum
     (Gray Collection)

Italy

GIORGIO MORANDI   Italy   1890–1964

149   *Still life*   1934
      Etching   11¾ × 15⅜
      Fogg Art Museum (Gift of Meta and Paul J. Sachs)

MARINO MARINI

Italy   1901–

150   *Juggler and horses, green
      background, yellow border*   1953
      Color lithograph
      23½ × 17⅝
      Fogg Art Museum

The Abstract Trend

WASSILY KANDINSKY

Russia   1866–1944

151   *Composition*   1922
Color lithograph   10 ¼ × 10
From *Kleine Welten*
Busch-Reisinger Museum,
Harvard University

152   *Ball and diagonal*   1922
Woodcut   10 ¾ × 9 ¼
From *Kleine Welten*
Fogg Art Museum (Gray Collection)

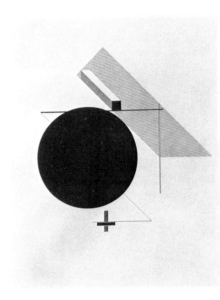

EL LISSITZKY   Russia   1890–1941

153   *Construction*   1923
Lithograph and collage   14 × 13 9/16
From *Proun Erster Kestnermappe*, no. 1
Museum of Modern Art, New York
(Purchase)

STANLEY WILLIAM HAYTER

England 1901– lives in France

154 *Tarantelle* 1943
Engraving and soft-ground etching
21 5/8 × 13
Fogg Art Museum

NICOLAS DE STAËL Russia 1914–1955 France

155 *The Wall* 1951 Color lithograph 10 5/8 × 18 7/8
Museum of Modern Art, New York
(Gift of Abby Aldrich Rockefeller)

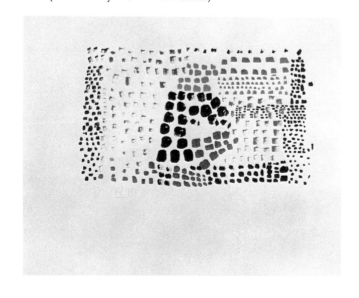

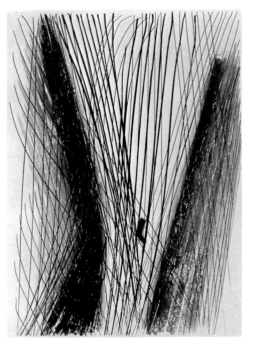

HANS HARTUNG

Germany 1904– lives in France

156 *Sheaf* 1953 Color etching and
aquatint 20 ⅝ × 15 ¼
Museum of Modern Art,
New York (Larry Aldrich Fund)

PIERRE SOULAGES

France 1919–

157 *Composition in blue and black*
1957 Color etching 26 × 19 ⅝
Museum of Modern Art,
New York (Anonymous loan)

JOAN MIRÓ   Spain   1893–

158   *Les Philosophes II*   1958   Color etching   12¾ × 19½
Fogg Art Museum

159   *Les Forestiers*   1958
Color etching   19½ × 12¾
Fogg Art Museum

K. R. H. SONDERBORG

Denmark 1923– lives in France

160 *Composition I* 1958
Color etching 23 ¼ × 13
Museum of Modern Art, New
York (Gift of Heinz Berggruen)

KAREL APPEL Netherlands 1921– lives in France

161 *Les Anges noirs* 1961 Color lithograph 22 ¼ × 30
Fogg Art Museum

JEAN DUBUFFET   France   1901–

162   *Work and play*   1953   Color lithograph   25 ⅞ × 19 ¾
Arnaud 168
Museum of Modern Art, New York (Larry Aldrich Fund)

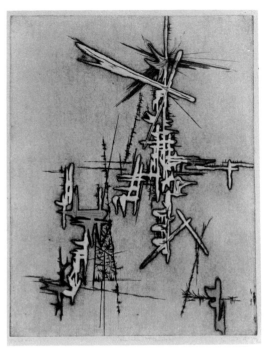

GABOR PETERDI

United States 1915–

163 *Sunken treasures* 1952
Relief etching and
engraving in color
17¾ × 14 From *Portfolio
of Five Prints*
Brooklyn cat. 72 c
Museum of Modern Art,
New York (Gift of
Rio Grande Graphics)

ROBERT RAUSCHENBERG

United States 1925–

164 *Stunt man I* 1962
Lithograph in blue 16 15/16 × 13 ¼
Museum of Modern Art, New York
(Gift of the Celeste and
Armand Bartos Foundation)

JASPER JOHNS

United States 1930–

165 *False start II* 1962
Lithograph in grays, black, and
white 18 × 13 ¾
Museum of Modern Art, New
York (Gift of the Celeste and
Armand Bartos Foundation)

GRACE HARTIGAN

United States 1922–

66 *Pallas Athena* 1961
Color lithograph 20 ⅞ × 14
Museum of Modern Art, New York
(Gift of the Celeste and Armand
Bartos Foundation)

Index of Artists, with Bibliography

PRINTED BY THE STINEHOUR PRESS AND
THE MERIDEN GRAVURE COMPANY